Where Is Everybody?

AN ANIMAL ALPHABET BY

Eve Merriam

WITH ILLUSTRATIONS BY

Diane de Groat

 ScottForesman

A Division of HarperCollins*Publishers*

ISBN: 0-673-80545-X
Where is Everybody? by Eve Merriam and
illustrated by Diane de Groat. Text copyright ©
1989 by Eve Merriam. Illustrations copyright ©
1989 by Diane de Groat. Reprinted by permission of
Simon and Schuster Books for Young Readers, a
division of Simon & Schuster Inc.

Child-sized version of *Where is Everybody?*
published 1993 by Scott, Foresman and Company,
Glenview, Illinois.

CELEBRATE READING! ® is a registered
trademark of Scott, Foresman and Company.

Printed in the United States of America.
    345678910-KPH-999897969594

**Scott, Foresman
and Company**

Editorial Offices:
Glenview, Illinois

Regional Offices:
Sunnyvale, California
Tucker, Georgia
Glenview, Illinois
Oakland, New Jersey
Carrollton, Texas

A lligator is in the attic.

Bear is in the bakery.

C at is at the computer.

D og is at the daycare center.

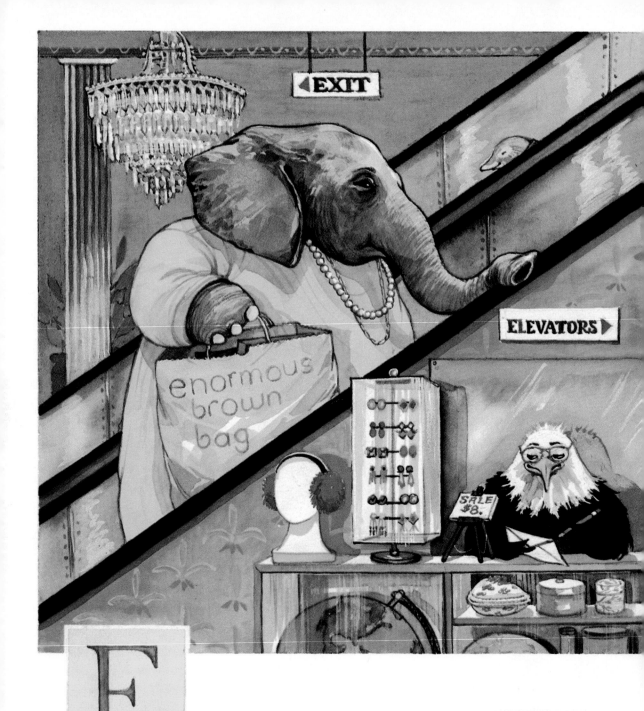

E lephant is on the escalator.

F rog is in the factory.

Giraffe is in the garage.

H

ippopotamus is in the hardware store.

I bex is on the ice.

J aguar is on the jungle gym.

Kangaroo is in the kitchen.

L ion is in the laundry room.

Monkey is in the market.

arwhal is in the noodle house.

O wl is in the opera.

Penguin is in the Post Office.

Quail is on the quarterdeck.

R abbit is on the roller coaster.

S heep is in the stroller.

Tiger is in the taxi.

U nicorn is underwater.

Vicuna is at the video store.

Walrus is at the wheel.

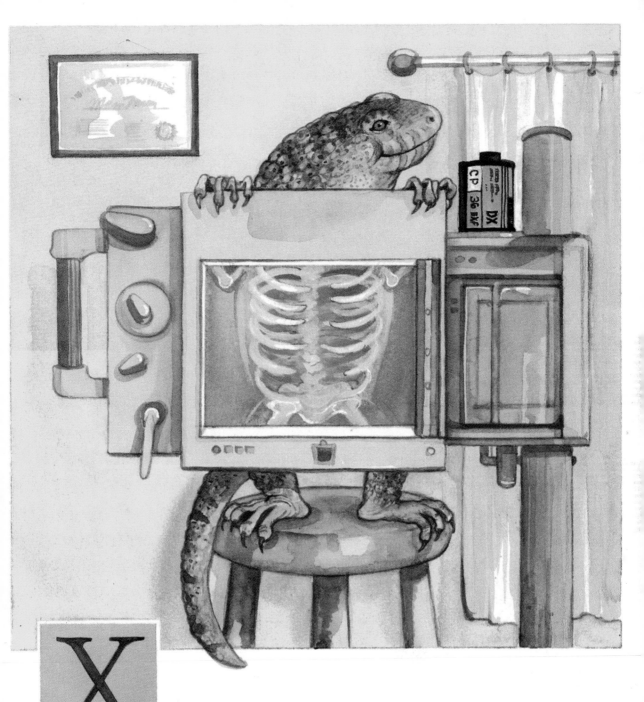

X enosaurid is at the X-ray
machine.

Yak is in the yard.

Z ebra is at the zoo.